Letterland

Phonics Practice 4

24 pages

Decodable text

Contains:
a_e, ai, ay
e_e, ea, ee, y (as in bab<u>y</u>)
i_e, ie, igh, y (as in m<u>y</u>)
o_e, oa, ow, kn
u_e, ue, oo, ew

✓ DfE Systematic Synthetic Phonics (SSP) validated

Name:

Silent Magic e

a_e as in make

1. Read the two words under each picture. Circle the word that matches the picture.

hat   hate

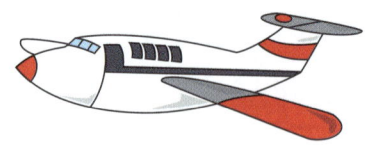

plan   plane

cap   cape

can   cane

2. Cross out the words that do not belong in the sentence.

The male / mill  has a thick man / mane .

3. Write a word for each picture.

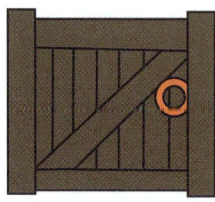         

_____   _____   _____   _____

ai as in rain   Mr A and Mr I out walking

1. Read the two words under each picture.
Circle the word that matches the picture.

train tram   ran rain   tail tall

paint pan   rain rail   sail snail

2. Read the sentences. Then colour the star next to the matching picture.

It is raining on the train.

He paints in the rain.

The chain is on the snail.

Mr A and Yellow Yo-yo Man out walking

ay as in say

1. Draw a pathway from Mr A and Yellow Yo-yo Man to the words that contain their sound. Write the words and cross out the other pictures.

tray

2. The Letterlanders are playing. Fill in the spaces with the words they might say.

| hay   day   play   tray   Sunday |

What _____ is it?

It is _____.

Let's _____ in the _____!

ea as in sea   Mr E and Mr A out walking

1. Read the two words under each picture. Circle the word that matches the picture.

      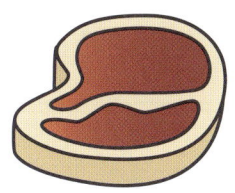

beach   beast   leap   lean   mate   meat

sail   seal   real   rail   mail   meal

2. The Letterlanders are having a picnic. Fill in the spaces with the foods that start with their sounds. Who says the last sentence?

bean   peach   cream   tea   treat

This is a cup of _____.

Can I pick a _____, please?

A plate of _____ salad.

Can I have a big _____ cake? A _____!

5

Mr E and Mr E out walking

ee as in bee

1. Read the names of these trees and label the pictures.

| Sleep Tree | Weep Tree | Sneeze Tree |
| Greet Tree | Beep Tree | Sweet Tree |

_____ _____ _____

_____ _____ _____

2. Read the sentences and write one of these words in the spaces.

feed   street   queen   teeth   sweeps

I must brush my _____.

We must _____ the sheep.

Shh! The _____ is asleep.

He _____ the _____.

y as in baby

Yellow Yo-yo Man works for Mr E

1. Write **y** on the lines to finish these Letterlanders' names. Yellow Yo-yo Man is working for Mr E.

Dippy   Edd_   Harr_

Samm_   Upp_   Vick_

2. Read the sentences. Then colour the star next to the matching picture.

That puppy is cosy.

What a funny baby.

Harry is happy when it is sunny.

He feels lucky.

Silent Magic e

i_e as in like

1. Add a Silent Magic **e** to the end of each word. Then read the words from left to right and match them to the pictures.

pine

slid_

rid_

bit_

2. Write a word to match each picture.

_____   _____   _____

3. Read the sentence and complete the picture.

Add nine stripes and a fine smile.

8

ie as in tie

Mr I and Mr E out walking

1. Read the two words under each picture.
Circle the word that matches the picture.

fly   pie

tie   time

kite   magpie

flies   fries

2. Cross out the words that do not belong in the sentence.

The   robin      fries   up and away.
      magpie   flies

3. Write a word for each picture.

_____   _____   _____

9

Mr I, Golden Girl and Harry Hat Man   **igh** as in night

1. Link **igh** to the words that contain their sound. Write the words and cross out the other pictures.

night

2. Read the sentences. Then colour the star next to the matching picture.

The kite is in flight.

The light is bright.

Max grabs Vicky tightly.

Nick has a nightlight.

y as in my

Yellow Yo-yo Man works for Mr I

1. Write **y** on the lines to finish the words. Yellow Yo-yo Man is working for Mr I.

by   sh_   wh_   dr_

tr_   fr_   sk_   fl_

2. Read the sentences. Then colour the star next to the matching picture.

It can fly in the sky.

Fred has five fish in pans to fry.

She tries to get dry.

Why is she shy?

Mr O and Mr A out walking

oa as in boat

1. Link Mr O and Mr A to the words that contain their sound. Write the words and cross out the other pictures.

goat

2. Draw a line around all the oa words in the word search below. They go across and down.

b	o	a	t	t	q	t
s	p	r	o	n	e	o
c	u	o	l	w	g	a
g	m	a	v	h	o	d
e	d	d	h	g	a	h
t	j	k	i	m	l	h

toad

road

boat

goal

12

ow as in show   Oscar Orange, Mr O and Walter Walrus

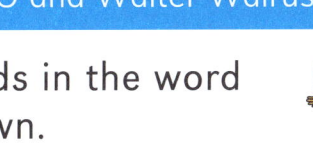

1. Draw a line around all the **ow** words in the word search below. They go across and down.

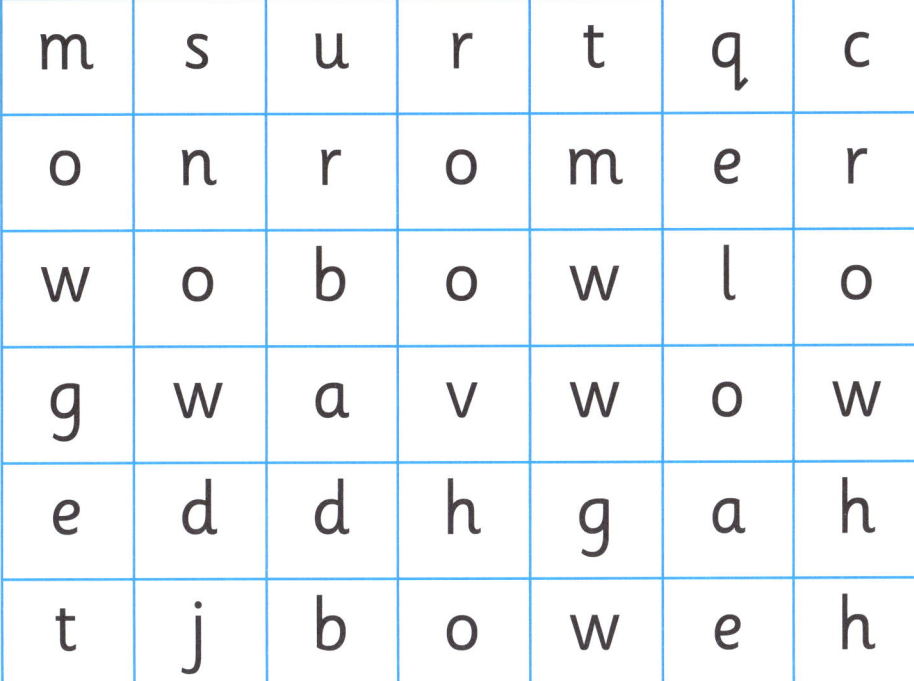

2. Read the two words under each picture. Circle the word that matches the picture.

slow grow   blot blow   tow throw

sow son   snow show   snow glow

13

3. Put these puzzle pieces together to make four longer words. Then write the words under the pictures.

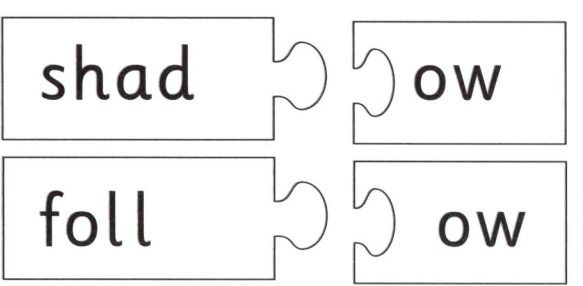
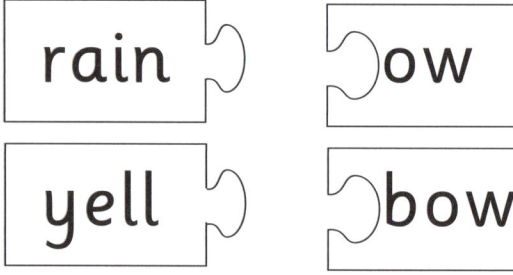

kn as in know

1. You can't hear Kicking King when he's next to Noisy Nick at the start of a word. Write the missing words in the spaces of this sentence.

Kicking King _____ that he cannot kick or bend his _____ next to Nick.

knee

knows

14

ue as in blue and cue   Mr U and Mr E out walking

1. Read the clues. Then colour the star next to the matching picture.

The glue is in a blue pot.

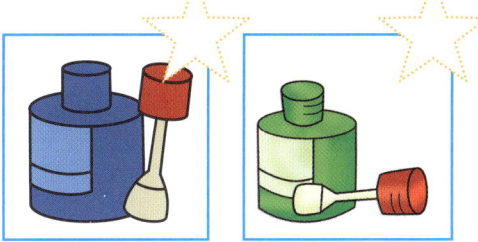

Help him! He needs to be rescued!

On Tuesday we went to the beach.

2. Put these puzzle pieces together to make four words.

stat	cue
res	ue
Tues	due
fon	day

The Boot and Foot Twins

oo as in moon

1. Link **oo** to the words that contain their sound. Write the words in the spaces. Cross out the other pictures.

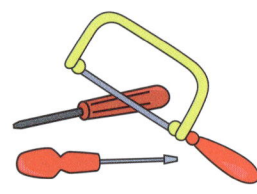

moon

2. Read the two words under each picture. Circle the word that matches the picture.

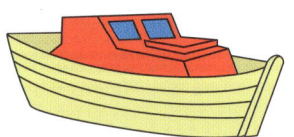

boat   boot   room   root   moose   moon

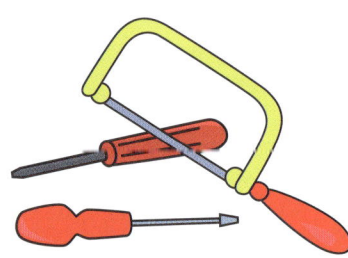

tune   tools   grass   goose   broom   boom

16

3. Write these oo words on the lines next to the object that makes the sound.

hoot   moo   zoom
toot   vroom

4. Put these puzzle pieces together to make two longer words. Then write them on the lines below the pictures.

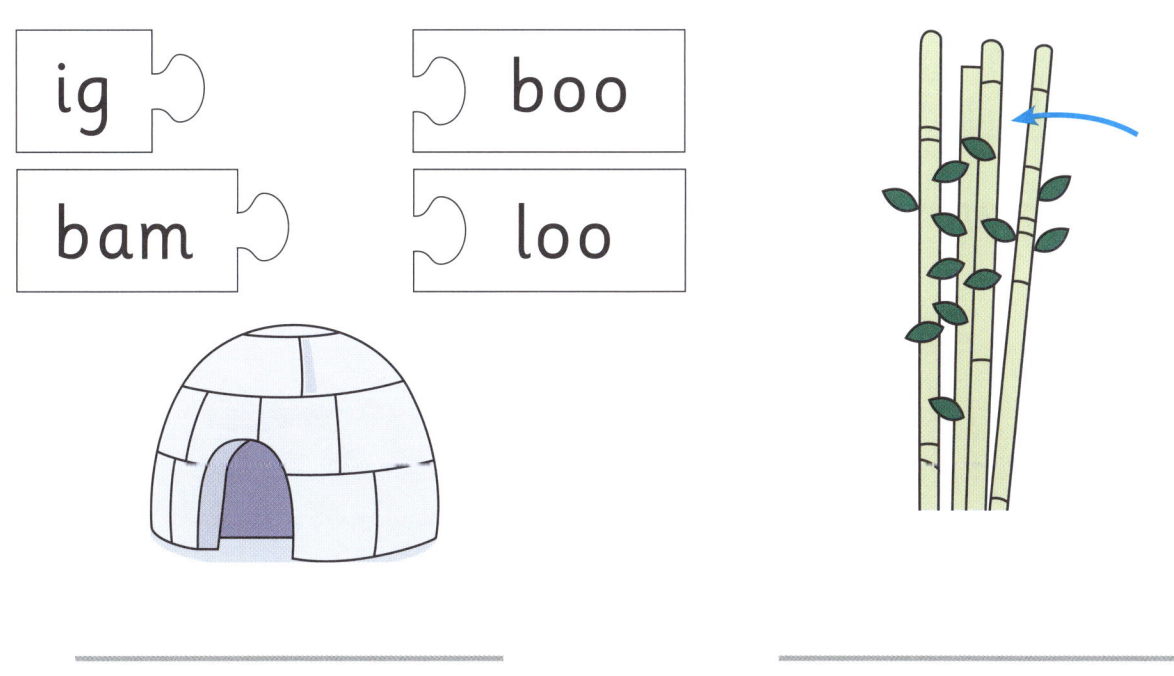

Eddy Elephant and Walter Walrus **ew** as in grew, few

1. Colour in Eddy Elephant and Walter Walrus. Then write **ew** on the lines. Read the words and match them to the pictures.

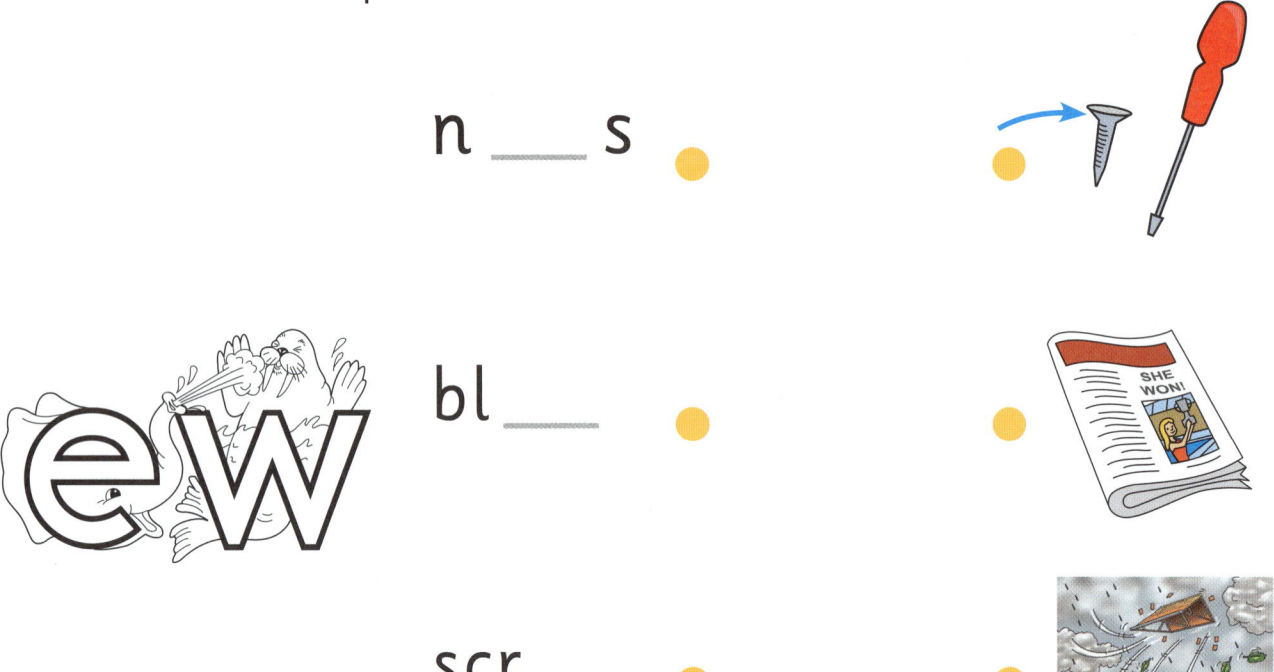

2. Read the two words below the picture. Circle the word that matches the picture.

3. Draw a line around all the **ew** words in the word search below. They go across and down.

c	r	s	d	t	q	s
h	s	t	e	w	e	h
e	u	v	l	w	p	r
w	n	e	w	s	a	e
e	d	f	h	g	o	w
i	s	c	r	e	w	s
s	c	b	v	e	o	h

shrew

news

screws

stew

chew

4. Some words sound the same but have different spellings and meanings. Fill in the correct words in gaps below.

| knew   new |

Nick went to a _____ club.

His mum and dad _____

he needed _____ boots.

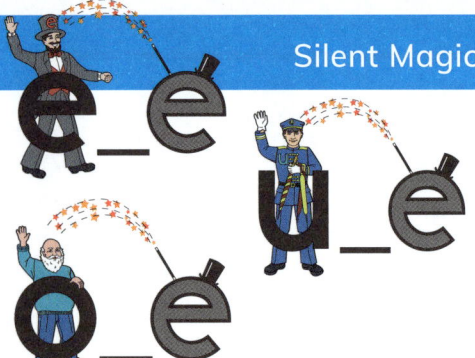

Silent Magic e   e_e, o_e, u_e as in these, home, cube

1. Read the two words under each picture. Circle the word that matches the picture.

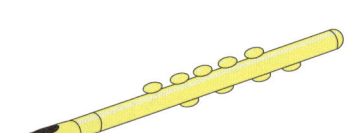      

lute flute   nose rose   doze drove

      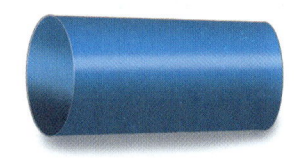

cub cube   rope ripe   dune tube

2. Read the sentences and write one of these words in the spaces.

| use   hole   these   cubes |

The mole ran back in his _____ .

Let's _____ this rope to make a swing.

Can we make a stack with _____ ?

I like _____ pens.

Revision

Silent Magic e

1. Read the words in the box. Sort and write the words by their spelling pattern.

drive	these	those	line	June
chase	home	date	delete	tube
complete	gave	tune	stone	quite

rope   pine   cube   cake

2. Write a word for each picture below. Then find a rhyming word and write it underneath.

| nine | snake | flute | Pete | rose |
| lake | complete | fine | nose | cute |

   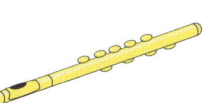

Review - Vowel Men out walking

1. Read the words. Then write them under the matching picture.

| blue | rail | flies | leap | soap |
| queen | goat | meal | pay |

leap

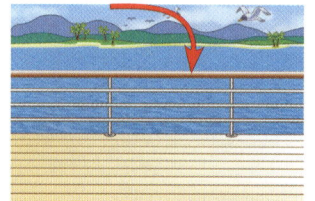

rail

meal

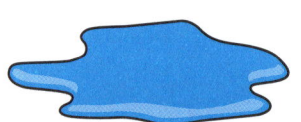

blue

goat

flies

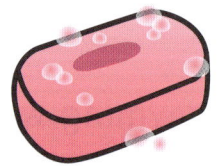

soap

queen

pay

2. Read the sentence. Then draw a picture to match.

A boat sails on the blue sea.

3. Label the animals in this scene.

seagull   sheep   foal
toad   magpie   goat   seal

4. Read the description and draw this beast!

A beast!

It has a blue coat, feet like a toad and green teeth.

How to use this book

On each page, read the instructions to the children. Discuss the pictures, as needed. Let them try and read all the words in the exercises themselves, as they are decodable. The workbooks are designed to consolidate and extend the teaching content of the Letterland *Phonics Teacher's Guide*.

Long vowels
Long vowel patterns require children to look beyond a single vowel letter to pronounce the sound of the vowel. This book teaches different spellings for some of the long vowel phonemes including the split digraph. By learning the story logic in the Letterland *Phonics Teacher's Guide*, children will have a child-friendly understanding of many phonic concepts, helping them read and spell thousands of new words.

Skills covered include:
- phonemic awareness
- decoding skills
- word building
- reading for meaning
- sentence completion
- using words in context when writing.

It is important to use this workbook:
- when children are not tired
- when there are no background distractions
- for short periods of time
- with plenty of praise and encouragement.

Correct handwriting positions

Left-hander

Fingertips 4cm
from tip of pencil

Elbows off the table
Feet on floor

Right-hander

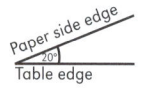

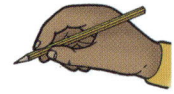

Fingertips 2cm
from tip of pencil

Chair slightly tilted
Feet on floor

Published by Letterland International Ltd.
8/10 South Street, Epsom, Surrey, KT18 7PF, UK
© Letterland International 2021
10 9 8 7 6 5 4 3 2

ISBN: 978-1-78248-554-4
Product Code: TP68

LETTERLAND™ is a trademark of Letterland International Ltd.
Printed in China.

All rights reserved. No part of this publication may be reproduced, stored in a retrieval system, or transmitted in any form or by any means, electronic, mechanical, photocopying, recording or otherwise, without the prior permission of the Publisher or a licence permitting restricted copying in the United Kingdom issued by the Copyright Licensing Agency Ltd, 90 Tottenham Court Road, London W1P 0LP. British Library Cataloguing in Publication Data. A catalogue record for this book is available from the British Library.

Sassoon Infant is a typeface designed for children learning to read and write.
© Adrian Williams Design Ltd

Written and designed by Lisa Holt
Consultant: Lyn Wendon, originator of Letterland

You may also like:

See our full range at: www.letterland.com

Please Note: These practice books match the teaching order in the Letterland *Phonics Teacher's Guide*.

For those who wish to follow a different teaching order the practice books can be used flexibly.

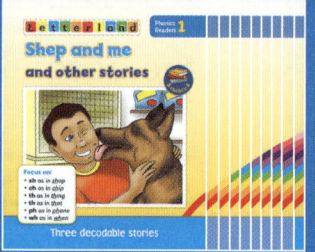